Stop Pot, Stop!

Popcorn

Jan Burchett and Sara Vogler
Illustrated by Charlie Fowkes

OXFORD
UNIVERSITY PRESS

is a department of the University of Oxford.
It furthers the University's objective of excellence in research, scholarship,
and education by publishing worldwide.

Text © Oxford University Press 2009

Illustrations: *Stop Pot, Stop!* © Charlie Fowkes; *What a Day* © T.S, Spookytooth

The moral rights of the authors, Jan Burchett, Sara Vogler and Damian Harvey, have been asserted.

First published 2009; this edition published 2009

Project X concept by Rod Theodorou and Emma Lynch

ISBN: 978-0-19-847667-2

Printed in China by Hing Yip

Paper used in the production of this book is a natural, recyclable product made from wood grown in sustainable forests.
The manufacturing process conforms to the environmental regulations of the country of origin.

At the school fair

Popcorn

Face Painting

Money

Popcorn

School Fair

Money

bric-a-brac

Jack's gran had a popcorn pot.

"Cook pot, cook!" said Gran.
Popcorn popped up from
the pot.

Jack put the popcorn into bags.

Money

Popcorn

"Stop pot, stop!" said Gran.
The popcorn stopped popping.

Jack sold all the popcorn.

Popcorn

Gran went to get a cup
of tea. Jack looked in the pot.

"Cook pot, cook!" said Jack.
Popcorn popped up
from the pot.

Popcorn

"Now I need to stop the pot," said Jack.

"Stop, pot!" said Jack — but
the popcorn went on popping.

"Pot, stop!" said Jack – but the popcorn went on popping.

"STOP POPPING!" said Jack – but the popcorn went on popping.

Gran ran up.
"Stop pot, stop!" she said.

The popcorn stopped popping.
"What a mess!" said Gran.

Thanks, Gran.

What a Day!

Damian Harvey
Illustrated by T. S. Spookytooth

OXFORD

Tizz went to the beach.

"I wish the sun was out,"
said Tizz.

The sun did not come out.
It started to rain.

Tizz put on his rain hat.

"Now I wish there was no rain," said Tizz.

The rain stopped. It started
to snow.

Tizz put on his big coat.

"Now I wish there was no snow," said Tizz.

The snow stopped. The wind started to blow.

Tizz put on his long scarf.

The wind stopped. Tizz sat
down. The sun came out.

"Now it is too hot," said Tizz.
"What a day!"

Match the word to the picture.

wind rain snow sun

Find out more

Read more about the weather ...

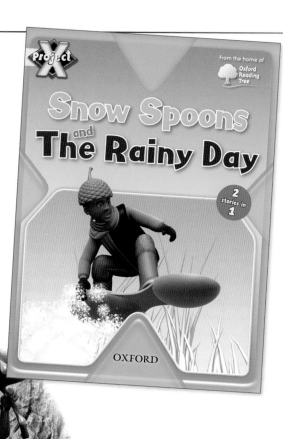